Dedicated to Autumn, Juliette, and Christian

It has special needs,

Thank you, eyes for allowing me to see,

Thank you, nose for letting me smell,

Thank you, mouth for working so well.

With lips to kiss, speak, whisper, and hum,

Thank you legs that skip, dance, wiggle and run.

Thank you, tummy for telling me when to eat,

Thank you, heart for never skipping a beat,

Thank you, hands that can have and hold

With fingers to touch, carry, shape, and mold.

Thank you, waist for letting me shake, shimmy, and twist,

Thanks for catching my fall, dear knees, bum, and hips!

Bodies come in all shapes and sizes,

And my body is just right.

Thank you, Body.

Made in the USA
Middletown, DE
26 June 2022

67824223R00015